W9-APJ-072

Clifford
Learns to Read

SCHOLASTIC INC.
New York Toronto London Auckland Sydney
Mexico City New Delhi Hong Kong Buenos Aires

Guess what, Clifford!" Emily Elizabeth said. I'm learning to read!"

And so she took
him to school.

"I learned my ABC's. Did you know that *Clifford* starts with a C? Reading is fun!" said Clifford.

"It's great to share a good book with friends!" said Emily Elizabeth.